Published by

ISLAND HERITAGE™
P U B L I S H I N G
A DIVISION OF THE MADDEN CORPORATION

94-411 KŌʻAKI STREET, WAIPAHU, HAWAIʻI 96797-2806
PHONE: (800) 468-2800 • FAX: (808) 564-8877
islandheritage.com

ISBN# 1-59700-245-3

First Edition, Eighteenth Printing - 2015

COP151906

Aloha is...

written by Tammy Paikai
illustrated by Rosalie Prussing

Dedicated with love to Wilder, Puamana, Ka'aina, Wainani
and my parents, Gerald & Melsa Takamatsu
— Tammy

For my 'ohana and sweet memories of Frany
— Rosalie

ISLAND HERITAGE™
PUBLISHING
A DIVISION OF THE MADDEN CORPORATION

Aloha is... how we say "Hello."

Aloha is...
what we say when we go.

Aloha means "love" in Hawaiian.
It's something we express, without even tryin'.

Aloha is...
saying "Have a nice day!"

Aloha is...
giving someone special a *lei*.

Aloha means you are kind and caring.
When you have a treat, you enjoy sharing.

Aloha is... helping one another.

14

Aloha is... pleasing your father and mother.

Aloha is... being hugged and kissed.

Aloha is... telling someone they are missed.

So be happy
and share a smile.

That is Aloha... "Hawaiian Style."

THE END